Charles M. Schulz

SNOOPY
and
THE PEANUTS GANG

BE PREPARED

ℛℛ
Ravette London

Printed and bound for Ravette Limited,
3 Glenside Estate, Star Road,
Partridge Green, Horsham,
Sussex RH13 8RA
by Mateu Cromo Artes Gráfica, s.a.

ISBN: 1 85304 011 8

"..ANXIOUS CHILDREN WRITING THEIR LETTERS TO THE "GREAT PUMPKIN," GROUPS OF PEOPLE GETTING TOGETHER TO SING PUMPKIN CAROLS...IT'S WONDERFUL!

THERE'S SUCH A JOYOUS SPIRIT TO THIS SEASON!

YOU REALLY BELIEVE ALL OF THIS, DON'T YOU, LINUS?

WITH ALL MY HEART, CHARLIE BROWN..

I BELIEVE THAT ON HALLOWEEN NIGHT THE "GREAT PUMPKIN" RISES OUT OF THE PUMPKIN PATCH WITH HIS BIG BAG OF TOYS!

OH, WHAT A SIGHT THAT MUST BE TO BEHOLD!

THEN HE FLIES THROUGH THE AIR TO DELIVER THE TOYS TO ALL OF THE CHILDREN WHO HAVE BEEN GOOD

IF YOU'VE BEEN BAD DURING THE YEAR, YOU DON'T GET ANY TOYS!

THAT'S UNDER-STANDABLE

EXCUSE ME A MINUTE, CHARLIE BROWN..I WANT TO GO INTO THIS STORE..

THAT'S FUNNY, THEY SAID THEY DIDN'T HAVE ANY...IN FACT, THEY SAID THEY NEVER HEARD OF THEM...

NEVER HEARD OF WHAT?

PUMPKIN CARDS!

THAT'S VERY DISAPPOINTING...

I HAD PLANNED TO SPEND THIS EVENING ADDRESSING PUMPKIN CARDS!

10-23

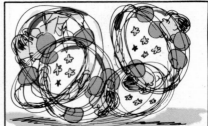

Tm. Reg. U. S. Pat Off.—All rights reserved
Capr. 1961 by United Feature Syndicate, Inc.

WELL, HOW DID THE SKIING GO?

I CAN TAKE IT OR LEAVE IT!

1-8

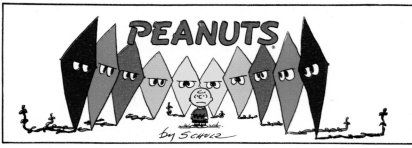

PEANUTS

by SCHULZ

THIS IS REALLY QUITE FASCINATING...

HAVE YOU EVER READ ANYTHING ABOUT "MASS COMMUNICATIONS," CHARLIE BROWN?

IT'S INTERESTING TO SEE THE EFFECT THAT T.V. PROGRAMS AND...

..AND THINGS LIKE NEWSPAPERS AND COMIC BOOKS HAVE..

..ON CHILDREN AND OTHER...

2-5

..AND OTHER PEOPLE, AND HOW WE SOMETIMES ARE LED TO BELIEVE THAT...

..THAT...

YOU'RE NOT LISTENING!

6-18

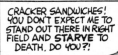

HOW'S THAT?

IS THAT ABOUT RIGHT?

SHE MUST THINK I'M A COMPLETE FOOL!

I'LL HOLD THE BALL, CHARLIE BROWN, AND YOU COME RUNNING UP, AND KICK IT...

EVERY YEAR SHE PULLS THE SAME TRICK ON ME!

WELL, THIS YEAR IT'S NOT GOING TO WORK! THIS YEAR I'M NOT GOING TO BE FOOLED!

Tm. Reg. U. S. Pat Off.—All rights reserved
Copr. 1961 by United Feature Syndicate, Inc.

WELL?

?

YOU THOUGHT I WAS GOING TO PULL THE BALL AWAY, DIDN'T YOU? WHY CHARLIE BROWN, I'M ASHAMED OF YOU! I'M ALSO INSULTED!

DON'T YOU TRUST ANYONE ANY MORE? HAS YOUR MIND BECOME SO DARKENED WITH MISTRUST THAT YOU'VE LOST YOUR ABILITY TO BELIEVE IN PEOPLE?

9-10

AUGH!

WUMP!

ISN'T IT BETTER THIS WAY, CHARLIE BROWN? ISN'T IT BETTER TO TRUST PEOPLE?

PEANUTS by SCHULZ

"WHEN SHE SAW THE LITTLE HOUSE IN THE WOODS, SHE WONDERED WHO LIVED THERE SO SHE KNOCKED AT THE DOOR. NO ONE ANSWERED SO SHE KNOCKED AGAIN."

WHAT DO YOU THINK WILL HAPPEN?

I CAN'T IMAGINE

"...STILL NO ONE ANSWERED, SO GOLDILOCKS OPENED THE DOOR AND WALKED IN. THERE BEFORE HER, IN THE LITTLE ROOM, SHE SAW A TABLE SET FOR THREE..."

"THERE WAS A GREAT BIG BOWL OF PORRIDGE, A MIDDLE-SIZED BOWL OF PORRIDGE, AND A LITTLE, WEE BOWL OF PORRIDGE. SHE TASTED THE GREAT BIG BOWL OF PORRIDGE..."

"'OH, THIS IS TOO HOT,' SHE SAID. THEN SHE TASTED THE MIDDLE-SIZED BOWL OF PORRIDGE. 'OH, THIS IS TOO COLD.' THEN SHE TASTED THE LITTLE, WEE BOWL. 'OH, THIS IS JUST RIGHT,' SHE SAID, AND SHE ATE IT ALL UP."

I HAVE A QUESTION!

10-1

ABOUT WHAT?

WELL, IT'S IN REGARD TO COOLING...IT WOULD SEEM TO ME THAT IF THE MIDDLE-SIZED BOWL WAS COLD, THE LITTLE, WEE BOWL WOULD BE COLD, TOO, RATHER THAN 'JUST RIGHT', AND..

POW!

I NEVER EVEN BROUGHT UP THE FAR MORE OBVIOUS POINT OF UNLAWFUL ENTRY!

PEANUTS
by
SCHULZ

10-22

WHATEVER HAPPENED TO THE GOOD OLD-FASHIONED NEIGHBORHOOD DOG?

PEANUTS
by Schulz

SIGH!

I DON'T THINK I'D MIND SCHOOL AT ALL IF IT WEREN'T FOR THESE LUNCH HOURS...I GUESS I'LL SIT ON THIS BENCH...

I HAVE TO SIT BY MYSELF BECAUSE NOBODY ELSE EVER INVITES ME TO SIT WITH THEM...

PEANUT BUTTER AGAIN! OH, WELL, MOM DOES HER BEST...

Tm. Reg. U. S. Pat. Off.—All rights reserved
Copr. 1961 by United Feature Syndicate, Inc.

THOSE KIDS LOOK LIKE THEY'RE HAVING A LOT OF FUN...I WISH THEY LIKED ME...NOBODY LIKES ME...

THE PTA DID A GOOD JOB PAINTING THESE BENCHES...

I'D GIVE ANYTHING IN THE WORLD IF THAT LITTLE GIRL WITH THE RED HAIR WOULD COME OVER, AND SIT WITH ME...

I GET TIRED OF ALWAYS BEING ALONE...I WISH THE BELL WOULD RING...

11-19

A BANANA...RATS! MOM ALWAYS...STILL, I GUESS SHE MEANS WELL...

I BET I COULD RUN JUST AS FAST AS THOSE KIDS. THAT'S A GOOD GAME THEY'RE PLAYING...

THAT LITTLE GIRL WITH THE RED HAIR IS A GOOD RUNNER...

AH, THERE'S THE BELL! ONE MORE LUNCH HOUR OUT OF THE WAY...

TWO-THOUSAND, ONE-HUNDRED AND TWENTY TO GO!

12-3

AAUGH!

HOW DOES HE **KNOW**? HOW DOES HE **DO** IT?!!!

HOW DID HE KNOW I HAD A COOKIE IN MY POCKET WHEN I WENT BY HIM THE SECOND TIME?

HE LISTENS TO YOUR FOOTSTEPS WITH THE COOKIE IN YOUR POCKET, YOU **WEIGHED MORE**!

THE ONLY WAY YOU CAN SURVIVE THESE DAYS IS TO KEEP YOUR EAR TO THE GROUND!

PEANUTS
by SCHULZ

OH, NO! DON'T TELL ME! NOT AGAIN!

HERE'S YOUR PIECE FOR THE CHRISTMAS PROGRAM..

"SO THE WORDS SPOKEN THROUGH JEREMIAH THE PROPHET WERE FULFILLED: 'A VOICE WAS HEARD IN RAMA, WAILING AND LOUD LAMENTS; IT WAS RACHEL WEEPING FOR HER CHILDREN, AND REFUSING ALL CONSOLATION BECAUSE THEY WERE NO MORE.'" GOOD GRIEF!!

MEMORIZE IT, AND BE READY TO RECITE IT BY NEXT SUNDAY!

I CAN'T MEMORIZE SOMETHING LIKE THIS IN A WEEK! THIS IS GOING TO TAKE **RESEARCH**

WHO WAS JEREMIAH? WHERE WAS RAMA? WHY WAS RACHEL SO UPSET?

YOU CAN'T RECITE SOMETHING UNTIL YOU KNOW THE "WHO," THE "WHERE" AND THE "WHY"!

I'LL TELL YOU THE "WHO," THE "WHERE" AND THE "WHY"!

YOU START MEMORIZING RIGHT NOW, OR YOU'LL KNOW **WHO** IS GOING TO SLUG YOU, AND YOU'LL KNOW **WHERE** SHE'S GOING TO SLUG YOU AND YOU'LL KNOW **WHY** SHE SLUGGED YOU!!!

CHRISTMAS IS NOT ONLY GETTING TOO COMMERCIAL IT'S GETTING TOO DANGEROUS!

12-17

AH! A PERFECT DAY!

ALL RIGHT, RISE AN' SHINE! IT'S RABBIT-CHASING TIME!!

OH, GOOD GRIEF!

THE SNOW IS FRESH AND THE AIR IS CLEAR...I PREDICT WE'LL SEE LOTS OF GAME!

HOW CAN YOU CHASE RABBITS IN THE MIDDLE OF THE NIGHT?

WE'LL START HERE...THIS IS A BIG FIELD, AND YOU SHOULD BE ABLE TO PICK UP THE SCENT WITHOUT...

Z

WAKE UP!

OKAY! WERE WE GO!!

3-4

SNIF SNIF
SNIF SNIF

SNIF SNIF
SNIF SNIF
SNIF

Tm. Reg. U. S. Pat Off.—All rights reserved
Copr. 1962 by United Feature Syndicate, Inc.

I GUESS WE'RE NOT GOING TO FIND ANY, SNOOPY, BUT AT LEAST WE TRIED...

EVEN THOUGH YOU'VE FAILED, IT ALWAYS MAKES YOU FEEL BETTER WHEN YOU KNOW YOU'VE DONE YOUR BEST!

I'D HATE TO DISILLUSION HER, BUT I DON'T EVEN KNOW WHAT A RABBIT SMELLS LIKE!

ALL RIGHT, LET'S HAVE THE INFIELDERS RIGHT OVER HERE...

GLASSES?! YOU'RE GOING TO WEAR YOUR NEW GLASSES WHILE YOU PLAY SHORTSTOP?!

WHY NOT? I'LL BE BETTER THAN EVER... I WON'T MISS A THING!

WELL, HOW ABOUT THAT BLANKET? DO YOU HAVE TO HAVE THAT WITH YOU, TOO?

DON'T WORRY ABOUT IT! SEE? I HAVE BOTH HANDS FREE! C'MON, HIT ME A GROUNDER!

3-18

WHOOPS!

Tm. Reg. U. S. Pat Off —All rights reserved
Copr. 1962 by United Feature Syndicate, Inc

THIS IS GOING TO BE ANOTHER GREAT SEASON!

STRIKE TWO!

STRIKE THREE

OH, NO!!!

YOU BLOCKHEAD! YOU DIDN'T EVEN SWING!!

YOU JUST STOOD THERE!

YOU BLOCKHEAD!

YOU STRUCK OUT, AND YOU LOST THE GAME!!

THEY'RE RIGHT... I'M A BLOCKHEAD... I LOST THE GAME, AND I DIDN'T EVEN GO DOWN FIGHTING.... I JUST STOOD THERE... THEY'LL NEVER FORGIVE ME....

MY TEAM IS NOT THE KIND THAT WILL LET YOU FORGET A MISTAKE...

THEY KEEP REMINDING YOU...

DAY AND NIGHT!

4-1

FORGET IT.... IT WAS A HOME RUN!

CAN I HELP IT IF MY HOUSE FACES THE BALL PARK?

PEANUTS
by
SCHULZ

IT'S KIND OF COLD TONIGHT...IT SHOULDN'T BE SO COLD THIS TIME OF YEAR...

I WONDER IF SNOOPY IS WARM ENOUGH...

I THINK I'LL TAKE MY SLEEPING BAG OUT TO HIM..

IF A PERSON IS GOING TO OWN A DOG, HE MUST LEARN TO ASSUME THE OBLIGATIONS OF THAT OWNERSHIP!

6-10

I'M GLAD I TOOK IT OUT TO HIM..HE SEEMED TO APPRECIATE IT..

I CAN SLEEP BETTER MYSELF NOW, KNOWING THAT HE'S WARM..

PEANUTS
by
Schulz

EXCUSE ME...

7-15

CLOMP!

!

THANK YOU VERY MUCH..

THINK NOTHING OF IT...YOU'LL HEAR FROM THE HUMANE SOCIETY FIRST THING IN THE MORNING!

SIT UP, SNOOPY, AND I'LL GIVE YOU A NICE PIECE OF CANDY...

HUMPF!

"SIT UP, SNOOPY, AND I'LL GIVE YOU A NICE PIECE OF CANDY"....PHOOEY! WHO NEEDS IT ?!

I GET SICK AND TIRED OF THEIR CONDESCENDING ATTITUDE!

WHY SHOULD I HAVE TO BEG FOR EVERYTHING? I'M AS GOOD AS THEY ARE! I DON'T NEED THEM! I CAN GET ALONG BY MYSELF!

7-22

OR CAN I ?

OH, GOOD GRIEF...HERE COMES CHARLIE BROWN..

I SUPPOSE HE'LL WANT ME TO PLAY BALL..."I'LL THROW THE BALL, SNOOPY, AND YOU CHASE IT!" *PHOOEY!!!*

?

SNOOPY?

9-16

?

I GUESS HE'S NOT AROUND.. I JUST WANTED TO TELL HIM THAT SUPPER WAS READY..

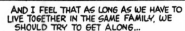

I'M SORT OF A FANATIC ABOUT SAVING THINGS...

YOU'VE NEVER SEEN MY LEAF COLLECTION, HAVE YOU, CHARLIE BROWN?

I'D LIKE YOU TO SEE IT... I'VE GOT HUNDREDS OF THEM, AND THEY'RE ALL MOUNTED IN BOOKS AND LABELED AND EVERYTHING...

I HAVE A BLACK WILLOW, A BUR OAK, A SHAGBARK HICKORY, A GINKGO, A QUAKING ASPEN AND A WHITE ASH...

EVERY TIME OUR FAMILY GOES ON A TRIP, I BRING HOME SOME NEW LEAVES... IF THERE'S ONE THING I'M REALLY PROUD OF, IT'S... ..

GANGWAY!!

YAHOO!!

...MY LEAF COLLECTION!

IT SNOWED LAST NIGHT..I CAN TELL!

HOW DISGUSTING! I GO TO SLEEP AT NIGHT, AND WHEN I WAKE UP, WINTER HAS COME!

NOW I WON'T BE ABLE TO FIND MY DOG DISH OR ANYTHING! RATS! WHAT DOES IT HAVE TO SNOW FOR?!

AT LEAST I THINK THIS IS SNOW...I CAN'T SEE... MAYBE THERE'S SOMETHING WRONG WITH MY EYES!!

12-2

MAYBE I WENT BLIND DURING THE NIGHT! MAYBE I...

AH! SNOW! SNOW! BEAUTIFUL SNOW!!

GOOD GRIEF! MY FEET ARE LIKE ICE!

I'M GOING TO HAVE TO DO SOMETHING TO HELP SNOOPY

HIS FEET GET AWFULLY COLD AT NIGHT..

HOW ABOUT A BLANKET?

BLANKETS HAVE A WAY OF SLIPPING OFF..

HOW ABOUT SOCKS? MAYBE HE COULD WEAR SOME WOOL SOCKS...OR MAYBE EVEN BOOTS...HOW ABOUT SOME BOOTS?

BOOTS! I THINK YOU HAVE SOMETHING THERE...

ther *Snoopy* books published by Ravette

lour landscapes in this series

st Serve	£2.95
ay Cool	£2.95
all We Dance?	£2.95
t's Go	£2.95
me Fly With Me	£2.95

ack and white landscapes

a Dog's Life	£2.50
undup	£2.50
ewheelin'	£2.50
e Cool	£2.50
gs Don't Eat Dessert	£2.50
u're on the Wrong Foot Again, Charlie Brown	£2.50

All these books are available at your local bookshop or newsagent, or can be ordered direct from the publisher. Just tick the titles you require and fill in the form below. Prices and availability subject to change without notice.

Ravette Limited, 3 Glenside Estate, Star Road, Partridge Green, Horsham, West Sussex RH13 8RA

Please send a cheque or postal order, and allow the following for postage and packing. UK: 45p for one book plus 30p for each additional book.

Name ....

Address ....

....